The Baroque Spirit

Selected, edited and annotated by Nancy Bachus

1600–1750

21 Early Intermediate to Intermediate Piano Solos
Reflecting Baroque Society, Style and Musical Trends

CD Track Listing

Second Edition
Copyright © MMVI by Alfred Music Publishing Co., Inc.
All rights reserved.
ISBN-10: 0-7390-0094-2
ISBN-13: 978-0-7390-0094-6

oreword

To understand and interpret musical style, one must recapture the spirit of the environment in which composers lived, created and performed. During the 17th to mid-18th centuries, opera, oratorio, cantata, sonata and concerto forms first appeared, and instrumental music became important. These forms reached their greatest height in the late-Baroque through the works of Domenico Scarlatti, George Frideric Handel and Johann Sebastian Bach.

Since the modern piano did not exist 300 years ago, most Baroque music was written for and performed on a harpsichord. Baroque composers seldom indicated dynamics, phrase markings, articulation, tempo or other performance instructions in general use today. As the music in this book will most likely be played on a modern piano by students, dynamics have been added along with slurs, staccatos, rolled chords and tempo indications.

When playing Baroque music, keep in mind

- there should not be a definite lift at the end of each slur (which would be correct for Romantic-style music). The reason for many of the slurs and staccatos found in Baroque music is to show the smaller patterns within a long line as it moves to its cadence.

- staccato notes should not be too short; their length varies according to the character of the piece.

- repeated phrases should be contrasted by changing dynamics, and sequential patterns should be shown through nuance and shading of the lines. In general, each ascending sequence increases slightly in volume and descending ones decrease.

Ornamentation

Baroque composers indicated some ornaments in the score but it was customary for the performer to also improvise ornaments. Frequently one composer's ornament charts contradicted another's in describing exactly how the ornaments were to be executed. In view of that and the fact that French and English composers of this period used unique symbols for ornamentation, the equivalent German symbols have replaced all others throughout this book.

Suggestions on Playing Ornaments

- Trills may vary in length according to context (and student's ability). Longer, more elaborate, even free trills are stylistically correct at the end of sections or pieces.

- Rolled chords should be rolled rapidly. Occasionally, arrows have been added to the roll indications to show their direction.

- The editor suggests first learning the music in this collection without ornamentation.

- It can be helpful to first play only one type of ornament, such as mordents, then gradually add other indicated ornaments without interrupting the rhythmic flow.

- A piece learned without ornaments can be re-studied at a later time to add ornamentation; it is essential that students first capture the character, rhythmic drive and spirit of the music.

Contents

Musical Style

Musical style comes through musicians as a result of their individual personalities and the characteristics of the times in which they live. Musical style differs according to:

- **who** composed the music.
- **when** it was written.
- **where** it was written.
- **why** it was written.

Louis XIV, King of France

© Planet Art

Baroque Style Period (1600–1750)

Maria Barbara, Queen of Spain, was a onetime student of Scarlatti.

The French word **Baroque,** derived from the Portuguese word *barroco,* means an imperfectly shaped pearl that was frequently used in jewelry at the time. In 1746 the term *barroco* was first applied to music in a derogatory way, describing it as rough and undisciplined; music that surprised listeners by its boldness: *"beauty… almost breaking the bounds of control."*[1] *Barroco* was replaced by the Italian term *baroco,* implying a sense of the bizarre, distortion, extravagant display and the overly ornate.

Political Settings: Italy, Germany, France, England and Spain

Baroque-style music began in Italy and spread throughout Europe. Political conditions in each country had a great effect on the music produced there.

- **Italy** was made up of small city-states, some independent but most ruled by foreign powers.

- **The Thirty Years War** in the early 17th century was very destructive to Central Europe, leaving **Germany** with over 300 separate states. The fighting was mainly between Protestant and Catholic powers, a result of Martin Luther's (1483–1586) Reformation in the previous century.

- After the Thirty Years War, **France** dominated Europe. King Louis XIV's (1638–1715) power is evidenced in his famous saying, *"I am the state."*[2]

- In **England,** Civil War led to the overthrow and beheading of King Charles I (1600–1649), briefly establishing a constitutional government until a limited monarchy was restored.

- **Spain** had a strong monarchy, and because its empire extended to the New World, for a time (late 1500s) it was the richest nation on earth.

[1]Frederic V. Grunfeld, and editors of Time-Life Records, *The Baroque Era* (New York: Time Incorporated, 1968), 4.

[2]William Fleming, *Art and Ideas* (New York: Holt, Rinehart and Winston, 1980), 277.

Three Baroque Keyboard Masters

J. S. Bach, G. F. Handel and D. Scarlatti are the three most well-known Baroque keyboard composers. Coincidentally, they were born in the same year.

Johann Sebastian Bach: born in 1685 in Eisenach, Germany—died in 1750 in Leipzig, Germany.

George Frideric Handel: born in 1685 in Halle, Germany—died in 1759 in London, England.

Domenico Scarlatti: born in 1685 in Naples, Italy—died in 1757 in Madrid, Spain.

Western Europe during the early 1700s

George Frideric Handel

Johann Sebastian Bach

GREAT BRITAIN

London

•Halle
Leipzig •
AUSTRIAN NETHERLANDS Eisenach

AUSTRIA-HUNGARY

FRANCE

SWITZERLAND

ITALY

OTTOMAN EMPIRE

•Madrid

SPAIN

•Naples

Domenico Scarlatti

Patronage

- Most Baroque composers and artists were employed by **patrons** of the arts. They composed and frequently performed whatever was required for a specific occasion. Most patrons were royalty, kings or aristocrats of smaller regions of Europe. Emperors, kings, popes and princes competed for artists to enhance their positions.

- Court musicians wrote extravagant operas and ballets as well as music for ceremonial occasions, background music, instructional music, and music for royal worship.

- With its headquarters in Rome, the Catholic Church was a major patron, and hired composers to write masses and motets for worship services. Protestant churches or "free" cities hired composers to provide music that might include cantatas for every Sunday of the year or music for civic events.

- A salaried group of musicians working for a patron was known as his **chapel,** and included singers, choir boys, organists and instrumentalists, with a *Kapellmeister* (maestro, maître) as the "master" or conductor in charge.

Baroque Art

- Michelangelo (1475–1564) foreshadowed the Baroque with his artwork on the ceiling of the Sistine Chapel.

- Baroque artists loved the large, grandiose and dramatic. Contrasting light and shadow increased the emotional elements.

- Baroque art seemed crowded with ornate columns and sculpture, and paintings filled with figures that gave the impression of movement.

Baroque Architecture

The Catholic Church, with inner reform, launched the **Counter Reformation,** trying to reach the spirit of the worshiper by dramatic impressions on the senses. Elaborate new churches with decorative altarpieces evoked awe, majesty and mystical devotion through ornate display and swirling upward movement.

Apollo (1666) by François Girardon (1628–1715)

© Planet Art

[3]Ian Crofton and Donald Fraser, *A Dictionary of Musical Quotations* (New York: Schirmer Books, 1985), 110.

The Norton Simon Foundation, Pasadena, California

Interior of Saint Peter's, Rome (1735) by Giovanni Paolo Pannini (Italian, 1691–1765) Oil on canvas 60¼" x 86½"

"Music hath two ends, first to pleas[e] the sence [sic],
...and secondly to move ye affections or excite passion."
Roger North (1651–1734), English lawyer, amateur musician and author,
The Musicali Grammarian (1728)[4]

Baroque Ideals

Baroque art and music include a wide variety of styles. If there is a unifying factor, it is in the search for deeper means of expression. Baroque artists strove to move or change the audience's **passions** or **affections.**

- These "affections" or "passions" were not the same as simple emotions. Artists recognized that people experience such states of mind as love, hate and wonder.

- They believed the body and mind tend to remain in one affection until a stimulus, such as music or art, changes it.

- Elaborate treatises were written on specific ways affections could be moved through music. The belief in music's power, even its obligation, to move the affections of the listener dominated the Baroque period, with the quality of an artwork judged by how strongly it affected the observer or listener.

The Teatro Regio at Turin during the Inauguration Night *by Domenico Oliviero*

Scala / Art Resource, New York

Baroque Opera

One way of moving an audience's affections was through the spectacle of elaborate, overwhelming **stage effects** in opera productions. Rows of columns, vaulting arches and domes were common on stage. Singers and musicians might descend as gods from the heavens on clouds. Sets, sometimes three stories high, might include fountains, statues and staircases. Enchanted palaces and entire towns were burned (in simulation) for grand finales. Some audience members conducted personal and political business in their boxes during performances, while others dined, played chess and sometimes slept.

[4]Joseph Machlis, *The Enjoyment of Music*
(New York: W. W. Norton & Company, 1977), 367.

Italian Musical Life

The area now known as Italy was divided into many separate states during the Baroque period. Courts of ruling families, smaller courts and large churches employed artists. "Lesser" courts might be relatives of ruling families, minor aristocrats, ambassadors, bishops and cardinals of the Church, or exiled kings and queens from other countries. Courts traveled seasonally between city and country residences, and sometimes went abroad spreading a wide variety of musical styles throughout Europe.

Italy in the early 1700s

Italy in the 1700s

Italian Opera

Baroque opera was developed in Florence, Italy, around 1600 by a literary club *(academie)* that was trying to deepen the expression of words through meaningful music. Two ways of setting solo songs developed: **recitatives**, a type of sung-speech that moved the story forward, and **arias**, which were more elaborate and lyrical in style.

■ Operas were performed for special occasions: royal birthdays or weddings, visits of foreign royalty or ambassadors and during Carnival season (just before Lent). A public opera house opened in Venice in 1637, and by the end of the 17th century over 350 different operas had been produced in its 16 neighborhood theaters.

[5]Ibid., 361.

"The Burning of the City of Argos," a scene from Cavalli's opera Hipermestra, *staged in Florence in 1658.*

Aria

Alessandro Scarlatti (1660–1725) was the leading composer of operas in Naples and Rome in the late 17th century. His influence spread to France, Germany and England. This *Aria* is from one of Scarlatti's keyboard *Toccatas*.

Alessandro Scarlatti
(1660–1725)

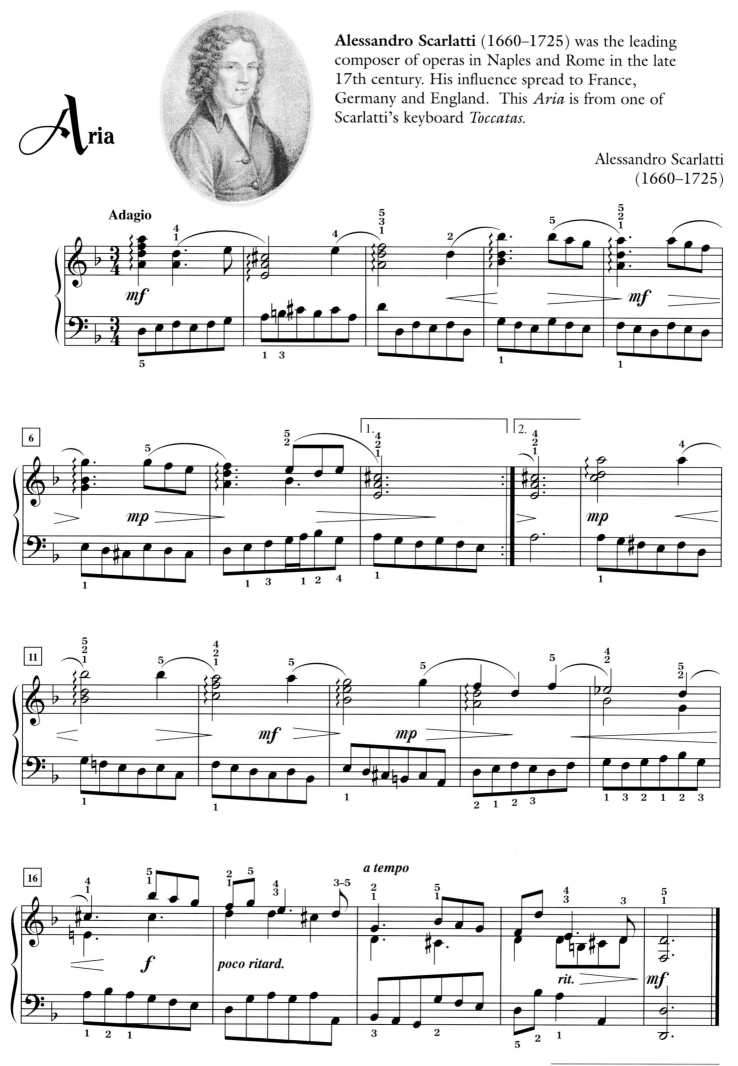

J. S. Bach's "Explication" in his own handwriting.
Courtesy of Yale University Music Library

"[Ornaments] are indispensable. ... [they] connect notes; they enliven them ... give a special emphasis ... make content clear, whether ... sad or joyful ... for true performance." Carl Philipp Emanuel Bach (1714–1788)[6]

Baroque Ornamentation

▪ Ornamentation was a vital part of Baroque music. Soloists were expected to "improve" their part with spontaneously improvised ornaments.

▪ Repeated phrases or sections were embellished, and improvising was a prized skill. Like decorations, ornaments are *"not necessary to the structure ... but [make] it more pleasing."*[7]

▪ Notated ornaments were usually abbreviated with special signs, which could be interpreted by the performer with personal taste and freedom according to context.

Keyboard Ornamentation

▪ **Italian** composers seldom notated their ornaments, expecting performers to improvise them.

▪ Seventeenth-century **French** lute composers indicated ornaments (*agréments*) by use of extensive and elaborate symbols; these symbols were carried over to harpsichord music. One French harpsichord composer used 29 different symbols. The executions of these ornamental symbols were specified and organized in tables in the composer's manuscripts. These tables were confusing and inconsistent since different composers often called identical ornaments by different names, and frequently used different explanations for the same symbols.

▪ French symbols were imported and adapted by many **German** composers, including Johann Sebastian Bach. His son, Carl Philipp Emanuel Bach (1714–1788), clarified these 17th-century French ornaments and their use with rules that were accepted until the time of Ludwig van Beethoven (1770–1827). After that, composers usually wrote out the ornaments as part of the music.

▪ **English** composers used an entirely unique set of symbols.

The following chart shows the accepted execution for frequently used Baroque ornaments; however, any of these realizations could vary within a specific musical context. Speed of execution depends upon the rhythm, tempo and character of the music.

Common Baroque Ornaments (German Symbols)

	Symbol	Beginning Note	Number of Notes	Direction	Rhythmic Beginning	Execution
Mordent	⬥⬥	written note	3	down	on the beat	
Trill	⬥⬥ or *tr*	note above	4 or more depending on the length of the ornamented note	down	on the beat	
Turn	∾	note above	4	down, then back up	where placed	
Combined trill & mordent	⬥⬥⬥	note above	6 or more	down	on the beat	

[6] *New Grove Dictionary of Music and Musicians*, s.v. "Ornaments" by Robert Donington (London: Macmillan, 1980), Vol. 13, 826.

[7] Jean Rousseau in 1687, quoted in Edith Borroff's *Music in Europe and the United States* (Englewood Cliffs, NJ: Prentice-Hall, Inc., 1971), 292.

Long Appoggiatura: (leaning note) is played on the beat, thus delaying the principal note by half its length. If the principal note is a dotted note, the appoggiatura takes two thirds of its length.

With ordinary and dotted notes:

Short Appoggiatura: occurs most commonly before fast moving notes. It can be executed as a "crush," played on the beat, almost simultaneously with the principal note.

With a chord:

The editor suggests first learning the music in this collection without ornamentation, and then adding as many indicated ornaments as possible without interrupting the rhythmic flow or musical content.

Italian Keyboard Music

Because opera was so popular in Italy, the harpsichord was primarily used as a part of the orchestral accompaniment or in smaller instrumental ensembles. Most opera composers wrote some **solo keyboard music** that could frequently be played on either the organ or the harpsichord. These pieces were intended mainly for private performance by patrons.

Variation: The Folia

- The folia was a harmonic pattern used in songs, dances and sets of variations for different solo instruments and ensembles during the Baroque period.

- Folia means "empty-headed." The original dance was so fast and noisy that dancers appeared to be fools or out of their mind.

- It evolved into a slow and dignified form, most commonly in the key of D minor.

- Some Baroque composers who have written variations on the folia include Italians Antonio Vivaldi (1678–1741), Arcangelo Corelli (1653–1713) and Domenico Scarlatti (1685–1757); Germans Johann Sebastian Bach (1685–1750) and Carl Philipp Emanuel Bach (1714–1788).

This harsichord was built by Lucca Giusti in 1677.

The eight-measure harmonic pattern is repeated with changes in measures 14–16, 31–32 and 47–48 to finalize the cadence.

Measures 1–8: | i | V | i |VII | III | VII | i | V |

Measures 9–16: | i | V | i |VII | III |VII i |iv V | i |

Folia

Alessandro Scarlatti
(1660–1725)

ⓐ The editor suggests all the trills in this piece begin on the upper note. See page 10 for further explanation.

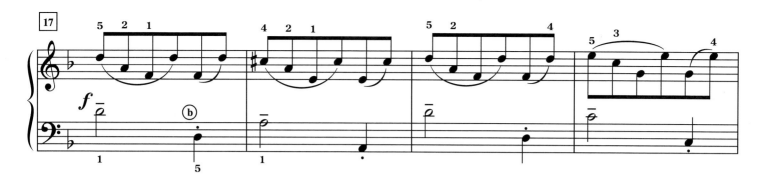

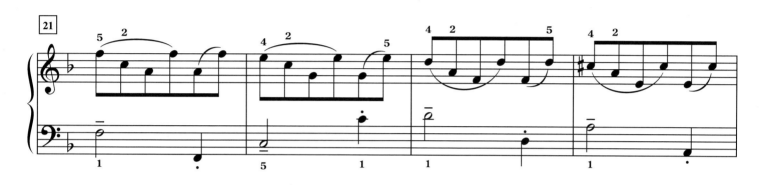

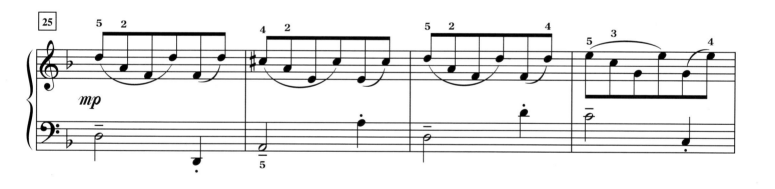

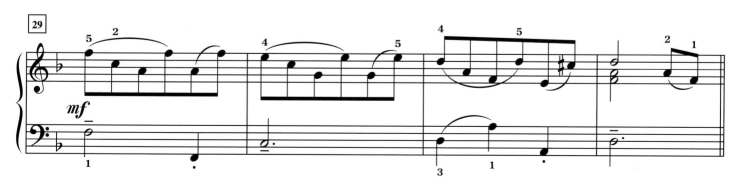

ⓑ The editor suggests that staccato notes not be played too short throughout this book. Their length varies according to the character of the piece.

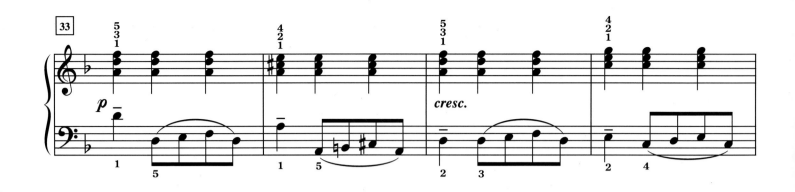

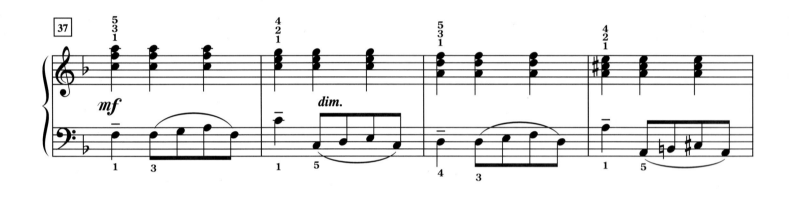

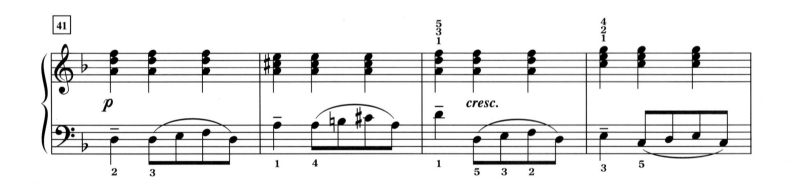

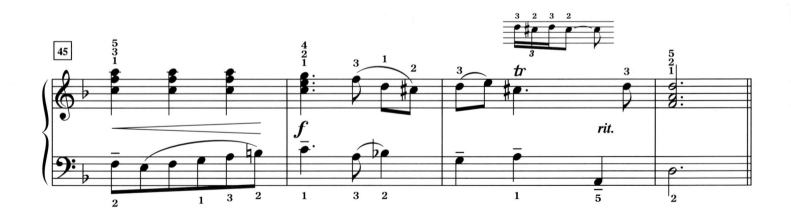

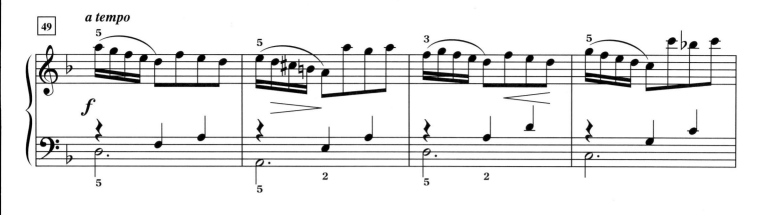

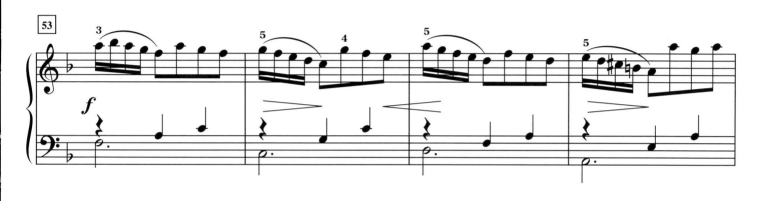

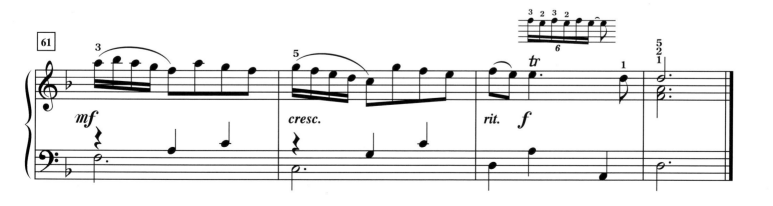

Venetian Influence

- Venice, located in Northern Italy, had many international visitors, including kings from Russia, Poland and Denmark, the Elector of Saxony and composer George Frideric Handel.

- With its three-month Carnival season (before Lent), Venice became known as the *"pleasure capital of Europe."*[8] Carnival in 1700 had 30,000 visitors in addition to 140,000 permanent residents.

- With two choir lofts, **St. Mark's Cathedral** developed a musical style using organ, several opposing choirs, and groups of instruments (violins, brass) spaced around the galleries of the church. This style became known throughout Europe and laid the foundation for the modern orchestra.

- Four state-funded orphanages had music instruction as part of their curriculum, developing many virtuosos and attracting influential visitors to concerts, where as many as 40 girls would perform (frequently from behind a lattice of ironwork for modesty).

- These institutions' fame as music conservatories became so widespread that European patrons paid to send musicians there to study. Venice became a "finishing school" for German composers and **Italian became the international language of music**.

- Antonio Vivaldi (1678–1741) was *maestro di cappella* (music director) at the **Pietà**, the most famous of the four establishments. He taught violin and composed for and directed chapel performances on Sundays and holidays. Concerts were presented there when the theatres were not in season.

[8]H. C. Robbins Landon and John Julius Norwich, *Music in Venice* (London: Thames and Hudson Ltd., 1991), 99.

Coronation ceremony of the Doge (ruler of Venice); the new Doge throws coins to the people on the Piazza di San Marco (St. Mark's Square). Painting by Gabriele Bella, early 18th century.

Baroque Musical Style

Stile Concertante (Concerto Style)

During the Baroque era, a new style developed known as the **concerto style** (*concertare:* to compete or fight side by side as "brothers-in-arms"). Concertos featured soloists (usually violinists) or groups of soloists, then called a **concerto grosso**, to display increased technical skill and real virtuosity.

The most important element in this style was **contrast**:

- *loud and soft*, with frequent "echo" effects, sometimes called **terraced dynamics**
- *high and low* ranges
- *fast and slow*
- *theme against counter-theme*
- *soloist(s) and **tutti*** (full orchestra or all instrumentalists playing)
- *free (sung-speech) rhythm* and ongoing, *metrical, dancelike rhythms*
- *changes in color* (different instruments or different keyboards)

Baroque Musical Structure

Motive

A **motive** is a brief fragment of a musical theme that is easily recognized. Here is the short motive (motive 2) in measure 26 of the following *Sonata in A Major* by Baldasarre Galuppi (1706–1785):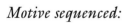

Sequence

When a motive or phrase is repeated at a different pitch, often a step higher or lower, it is called a **sequence**. In measures 26–28 of the Galuppi *Sonata in A Major*, the motive is sequenced four times.

Motive sequenced:

Longer motive (measures 17–18) and its three sequences (measures 19–24):

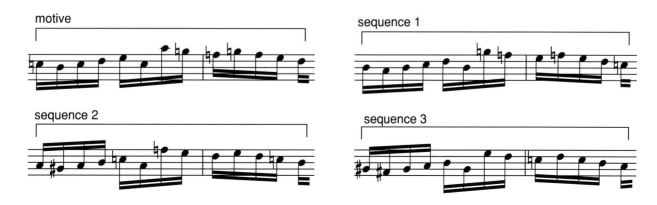

Keyboard Sonata: Binary Form

Sections:	‖: A :‖‖: B :‖
Key relationships:	‖: I :‖‖: V :‖

- Most Baroque keyboard sonatas are single movements in **binary form**, with two parts that are usually repeated. They normally **modulate** (change key) at the end of the first part to a closely related key, which is most often the **dominant** (a fifth higher than keynote) or **relative major or minor**. The second part begins in the new key and returns to the beginning key to end.

Rounded Binary Form

The Galuppi *Sonata in A Major* is in **rounded binary form**:

- It is in two parts, with each part repeated (binary form).

- It begins in A major, modulates to A minor (the parallel minor) at the end of the **A** section and concludes in A major.

- It is called a "rounded" binary because the opening theme returns in measure 30 of the **B** section.

Sections:	‖: A :‖‖: B :‖
Themes:	‖: a :‖‖: b a :‖
Key relationships:	‖: I i :‖‖: i I :‖
	‖: A Am :‖‖: Am A :‖

Baldasarre Galuppi was born on an island near Venice. His father, a violinist at a local theater, was his first teacher. After his opera was hissed off the stage in Venice, he enrolled in one of the four conservatories there for serious study. He eventually became the director of that conservatory and had a successful career as an opera composer throughout Italy, England and Russia, where he also served for a time as Director of the Chapel at the Court of Catherine the Great (1729–1796). He wrote over 100 operas, 27 oratorios, over 90 keyboard sonatas and served as *maestro di cappella* at St. Mark's Cathedral. Robert Browning (1812–1889) immortalized him in a poem entitled *A Toccata of Galuppi's.*

Sonata in A Major

SECTION A

Allegretto

Baldasarre Galuppi
(1706–1785)

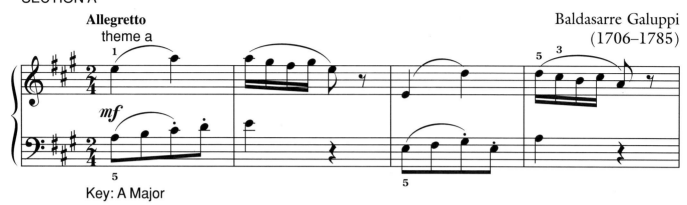

Key: A Major

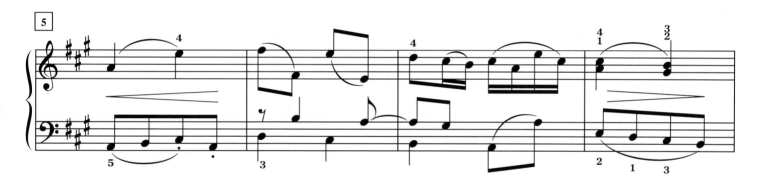

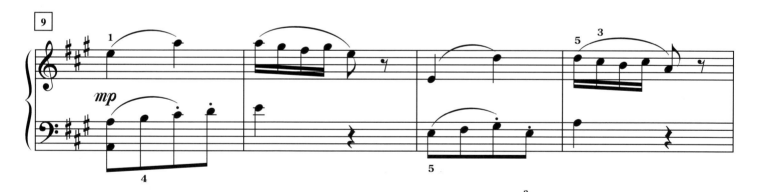

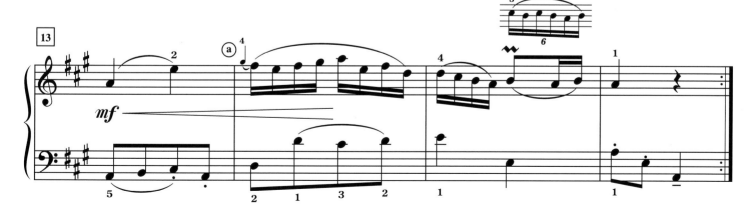

ⓐ   The editor suggests playing the short appoggiaturas in measures 14, 17, 19, 21, 23 and 43 as a "crush," on the beat almost simultaneously with the main note. See page 10 for explanation.

SECTION B
theme b

Key: A Minor

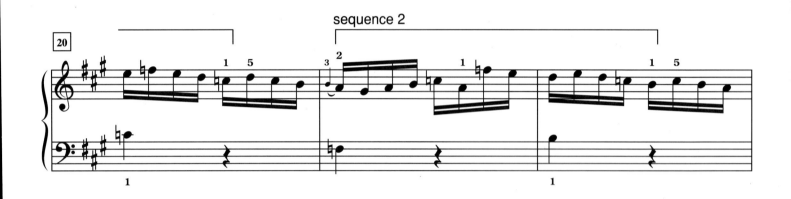

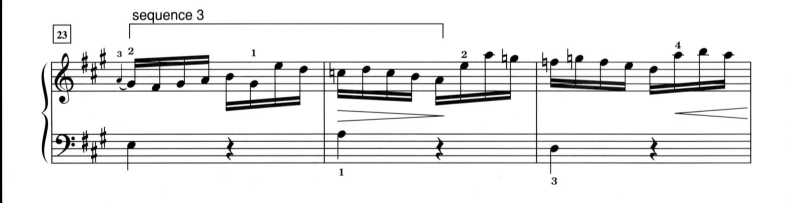

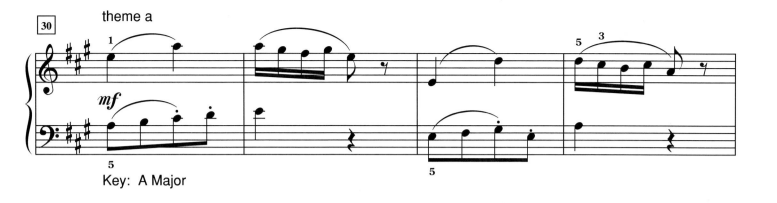

theme a

Key: A Major

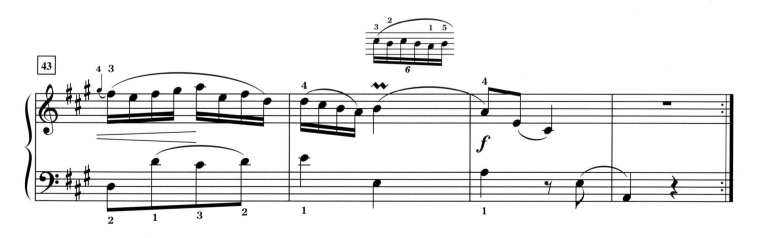

Giovanni Battista Pescetti was born in Venice and his first opera, a collaboration with Baldasarre Galuppi, was produced there in 1728. Pescetti settled in England in 1738; one year later, nine of his harpsichord sonatas were published in London. He became the director of the Covent Garden Theater, but his final years were spent in Venice as organist at St. Mark's Cathedral.

Pescetti's *Sonata in C Minor* is in typical **binary form.** It begins in C minor, modulates to E-flat major at the end of the **A** section (the relative major) and concludes in C minor.

Sonata in C Minor

SECTION A

Giovanni Battista Pescetti

(1704–1766)

SECTION B

Key: E-flat Major

Key: C Minor

motive

sequence 1

sequence 2

sequence 3

ⓐ The editor suggests playing the short appoggiaturas in measures 59 and 66 as a "crush," on the beat almost simultaneously with the main note. See page 10 for explanation.

Dance: Gavotte

Originally a French folk dance, the **gavotte** became a **popular instrumental form** and was a regular part of formal court balls during the Baroque period. A joyful dance in duple meter, it had "springing" steps and needed a spacious feeling and moderate tempo for performance.

Arcangelo Corelli, a composer, violinist, violin teacher and director of ensembles, worked for a series of patrons in Rome. He was the first composer to gain fame as a composer of only instrumental works.

The best violinist of his day, he brought string playing to new heights, requiring new levels of bowing and fingerboard techniques in his compositions. Some of his collections of sonatas, trios and concertos were published in over 40 editions. Among the first "classics," they were studied, played and imitated throughout Europe.

Arcangelo Corelli
(1653–1713)

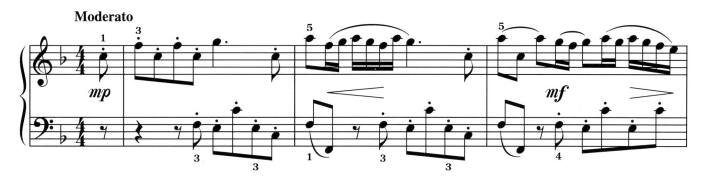

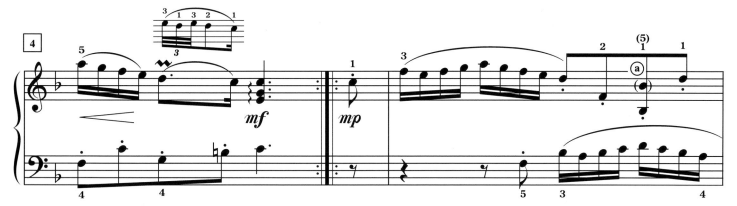

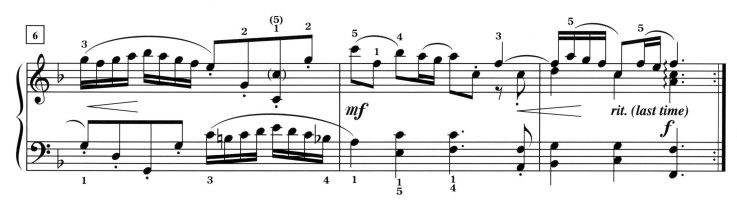

ⓐ If the leaps are too difficult on beat 4 of measures 5 and 6, the editor suggests playing notes an octave higher than written (as indicated in parentheses).

Fugue Style

A **fugue** ("fleeing" or "chasing") is written in **contrapuntal style**, a texture with a number of independent voices. Fugue has been called a **style**, even a texture, rather than a form since it can be found within sonatas and other larger works. The ability to write in fugue style is difficult and has been a part of compositional studies for over 200 years.

- A fugue has **one main theme or subject**, first played alone, then stated in the other voices.

- The **statements of the subject** usually enter at different pitches (I and V), in **imitation** of each other.

- **Episodes**, sections where there is no complete fugue subject in any voice, frequently have **motives** and **sequences**.

The fugue subject in the Fughetta in E Minor of Zipoli:

Domenico Zipoli, an organist at a Jesuit church in Rome, wrote a mass, oratorios and motets. A collection of his works for organ and harpsichord were published in Rome. After deciding to become a missionary in Paraguay, he traveled to Argentina for three years to train in philosophy and theology. The most famous Italian composer to go to the New World in colonial times, Zipoli completed his studies there but died of tuberculosis before receiving his priest's orders. His music was much in demand in South America and was also published in London and Paris.

Fughetta in E Minor

Domenico Zipoli
(1688–1726)

Allegretto

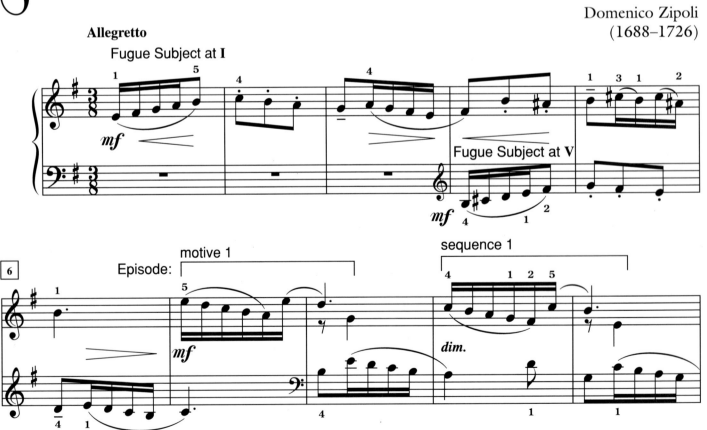

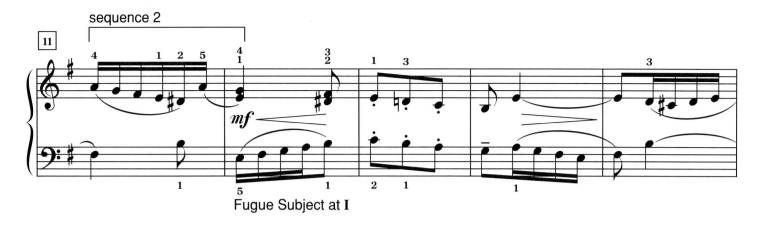

sequence 2

Fugue Subject at **I**

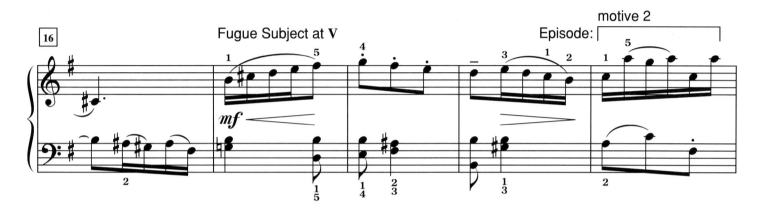

Fugue Subject at **V**

Episode:

motive 2

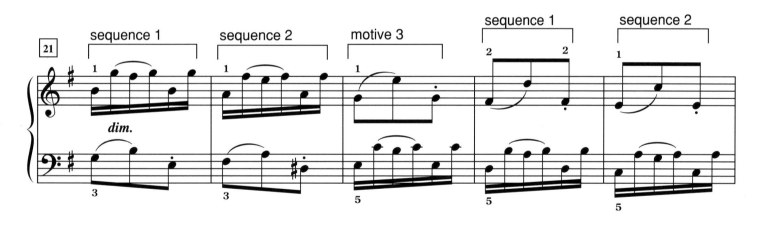

sequence 1

sequence 2

motive 3

sequence 1

sequence 2

dim.

Variation of
Fugue Subject at **V**

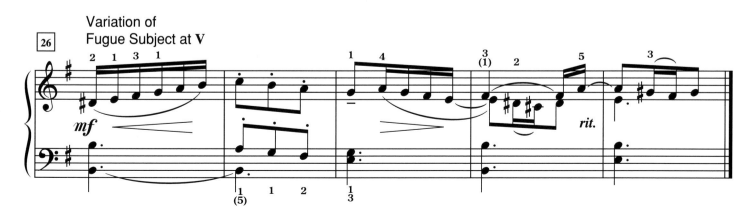

rit.

Baroque Keyboard Instruments

Church organist

The Organ

- It produced sound by air blown through pipes. A keyboard operated valves that controlled the air flow.

- It usually had three keyboards (manuals), each controlling a complete set of pipes, which produced different types of sounds.

- The organ had a pedal keyboard, which controlled bass pipes.

The Clavichord

- It was used primarily in homes (the "poor man's keyboard").

- It sounded by a metal tangent striking a string, so finger energy could create subtle dynamic changes.

- It had a dynamic range from only about *ppp* to *p*; the "striker" remained on the string, so it also muffled and dampened the sound.

- It could make a kind of vibrato, known as **bebung**, if the player moved his finger up and down on a key.

- The clavichord was the most intimate and expressive keyboard instrument, *"the thrilling confidant of solitude."*[9]

Young woman playing a clavichord

The Harpsichord

- It was the most widely used stringed keyboard instrument in the Baroque period.

- It had one or two keyboards, about five octaves in length, each with three or four sets of strings, which varied in pitch and tone quality.

- It had hand stops or levers to combine sets of strings or keyboards and vary tone.

- The harpsichord found most frequently in homes was smaller and was known as a **spinet** or **virginal**.

- It sounded when strings were plucked by small quills on a jack (plectra), so true crescendo or diminuendo was impossible.

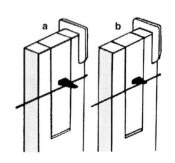

The plectra of a harpsichord plucking the string:

  a. in normal position (center of plectra)
  b. in a lute stop (the tip, creating a more brittle tone quality)

[9]Dominic Gill, ed., *The Book of the Piano* [Oxford: Phaidon Press Ltd., 1981]
(Ithaca, NY: Cornell University Press, 1981), 99.

The Pianoforte

- It was invented in Florence, Italy around 1700 by **Bartolomeo Cristofori** (1655–1731).

- It was called a *gravicembalo col piano e forte* (harpsichord with soft and loud).

- It produced sound when a hammer struck the string and a mechanical **escapement** allowed the hammer to fall back.

- The pianoforte did not come into wide use until after 1750, with pianos built primarily in Germany and Austria (using Cristofori's piano action).

Cristofori's Pianoforte

Baroque Instrumental Ensembles/Early Orchestras

String Instruments

Violin-making reached its height between 1650 and 1750 in Cremona, Italy. The instruments built by **Antonio Stradivari** (1644–1737) and **Giuseppe Guarneri** (1698–1744) are still preferred by many violinists today. Due to their quality and scarcity, these instruments sometimes sell for over a million dollars.

Harpsichords as Part of the Ensemble—*basso continuo (figured bass)*

Emphasis on moving outer lines (frequently played by violin and cello) with a harmonic interior became the favored Baroque texture.

Basso continuo (continuous bass):

- was a **shorthand notation of numbers** under the bass line.

- numbers **indicated the chords** to accompany the written melody.

- usually required **two performers**:

  1. one player improvising ("realizing") the **chord harmonies** from the numbered bass line, at a harpsichord, organ, lute or guitar;

  2. one playing the **numbered bass line** on a cello, gamba or bassoon.

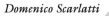

Spanish Musical Life

Operas and theatrical spectacles were rare in Spain until the late-17th century because the Queen considered them improper and the King preferred dancing. Full-blown European Baroque-style music was imported by foreign composers to the Royal Court from the Spanish possessions of Milan and Naples (Italy), by other Italian musicians from Vienna, and by French musicians from the Court of Louis XIV. Native composers and music remained more popular with the public, who rejected Italian opera. Ferdinand VI and his wife, Maria Barbara, supported Italian opera for their private pleasure and traveled from one royal site to another with their singers, orchestra and other musicians.

Domenico Scarlatti (1685–1757)

At age 16, Domenico Scarlatti was appointed organist and composer at the Royal Chapel in Naples, Italy, where his father, Alessandro, was *maestro di cappella* (Chapelmaster). While living in Italy, Scarlatti spent time at the Medici Court in Florence and lived in Venice for four years. In Rome, he had a keyboard "duel" (a contest in virtuosity) with George Frideric Handel; Scarlatti was declared the winner on the harpsichord while Handel conquered on the organ.

In 1719, he became the Master of the Chapel of the Royal Court in Lisbon, Portugal. One of his duties was the keyboard training of King John V's talented daughter, the Infanta Maria Barbara, and her younger brother. In 1728, when Maria Barbara married the Spanish Crown Prince Fernando, Scarlatti also moved to Madrid and performed whatever musical duties Maria Barbara assigned.

Scarlatti spent the last 28 years of his life at the Spanish Court of Ferdinand VI. He wrote operas, oratorios, cantatas and other vocal and instrumental works, but he is most famous for over 550 binary keyboard sonatas he composed while living in Spain.

Ferdinand VI and Maria Barbara of Spain in an opera setting. Domenico Scarlatti and the famous Italian opera singer, Farinelli, are among the musicians in the gallery in the upper right.

Sonata in G Major

"When we hear [Domenico] Scarlatti's music, we know that we are in the climate of sunlight and warmth.
It is Italy, it is Spain—the spirit of the Latin countries ..."
Wanda Landowska (1879–1959), harpsichordist[10]

Domenico Scarlatti (1685–1757)
K. 431

[10]Derek Watson, ed. introduction and selection, *Dictionary of Musical Quotations*
(Ware Hertfordshire: Cumberland House, Wordsworth Editions Ltd., 1994), 226.

Louis XIV as the "rising sun" in the Ballet of the Night, *Paris, Theatre Petit Bourbon, Spring 1654. Color lithograph by Maurice Leloir, 19th century.*

AKG London

French Musical Life

In France, music was part of military pageantry (including battlefields) and state occasions with visiting dignitaries, and was heard on barges, during hunts, coronations and funerals. Extravagant royal spectacles combined drama, vocal music, dance, processions, costumes, and stage effects created by machines and fireworks, with much of it designed to glorify the King and impress the world with his greatness.

Louis XIV (1638–1715)

Music in France reached its height during the reign of Louis XIV, who ruled for over 50 years and was a great patron of the arts. He and the other French kings of this period encouraged the development of a truly French style in music, but Italian music still had influence. Louis XIV personally played lute, harpsichord and guitar; he sang, composed, was an outstanding ballet dancer, and was almost obsessively preoccupied with music. Louis XIV had music rooms and theaters in all his palaces. Music was part of his everyday life—while he dressed, ate, said Mass as well as while walking or boating. He personally selected the subjects of ballets and operas that were heard in his court, supervised activities of his over 150 court musicians, and developed his children's musical tastes. He also danced the role of Apollo,[11] the Sun God in the Ballet of the Night. The sun was the official emblem chosen for him before his birth, and signaled the dawn of a golden era. (At this time, the skills of riding, fencing and dancing were required for a nobleman.)

[11]Apollo was also the god of music, the ruler of the planets and the sun.

Jean-Philippe Rameau (1683–1764), one of the leading French musicians of the 18th century, was known as a theorist, an opera composer, an important composer of harpsichord pieces and for his brilliance at improvising on a figured bass. He spent four years in Italy and fused many Italian and French elements in his operas. He wrote the *Traité de l'harmonie*, an important treatise that is still the basis of study for tonal harmony. In the 1740s he became a part of the Court of Louis XV in Versailles. Many of his operas and ballets included a **tambourin.**

A tambourin:

- was a lively dance, usually in $\frac{2}{4}$, popular in French theater.

- was based on a folk dance from Provence that was accompanied by **pipe** (fipple flute[12] played in one hand) and **tabor** (side drum with snare).

- had sharp rhythmic accents in the bass, imitating the **tabor**.

- had a bass line usually repeating a single note, most commonly the tonic.

- had a fast-moving melody in the upper voice imitating the **pipe**.

Tabors varied in size and shape. The upper head of the drum is fitted with a snare, and the drum is beaten with a stick.

A 17th century pipe and tabor player. Both instruments were played by one person.

[12]This flute family directs the air stream against a sharp edge (fipple), and includes whistles and recorders.

Tambourin

Jean-Philippe Rameau
(1683–1764)

Jean-Baptiste Lully was one of the leading French musicians of his day. An Italian by birth (Giambattista Lulli), he went to France at age 14 and spent the rest of his life there.

- He met Louis XIV when they both danced in the *Ballet of the Night*. Lully was soon in charge of composing court ballets and instrumental music and was promoted to "Master of Music for the Royal Family."

- He developed a truly French style of opera that integrated ballets, frequently danced by the King. The precision of the music and dance performances; the lavish sets, stage machinery and costumes; and the large vocal and orchestral forces were unequaled, and became the envy of every court in Europe.

Lully's music was performed throughout Europe, and Italian, English and German composers came to Paris to study with him. While conducting more than 150 musicians in a performance celebrating the king's recovery from an operation, Lully hit his toe with the long staff he used to beat time and died of gangrene shortly after.

Menuet

Jean-Baptiste Lully
(1632–1687)

Andantino

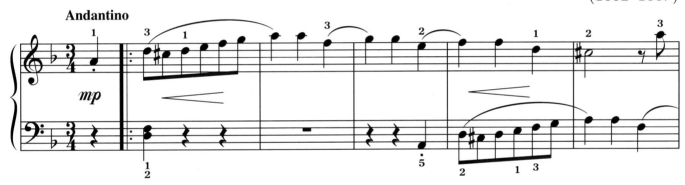

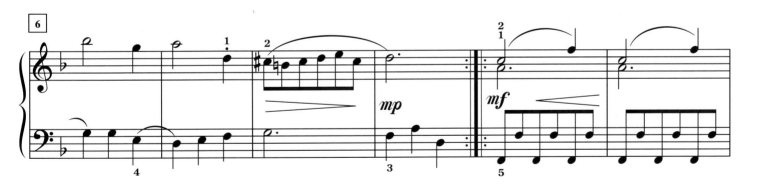

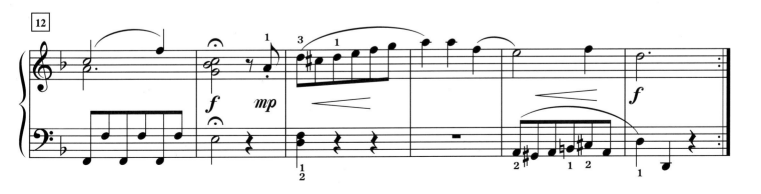

French Keyboard Music

A distinctive French style of harpsichord music was developed to entertain court society. Some of this solo harpsichord music was for the King at Versailles, but even more was heard at private concerts in Paris sponsored by lesser nobility, the wealthy middle class and musicians themselves.

By the early 18th century the Parisian salons were becoming an important part of French society, ushering in a new era of less formal music-making that frequently featured lute, guitar and keyboard soloists.

Characteristics of the French harpsichord pieces of this time are broken chords *(style brisé)*, profuse ornamentation, whimsical titles *(Tender Melody, The Little Nothing)*, and dance movements in binary form.

Louis XIV converted his father's hunting lodge at Versailles into the most lavish palace in Europe, and in 1682, the Court moved there from Paris.

AKG London

*Versailles Palace (built from 1661 on). Bird's-eye view of the palace and gardens (detail).
Painting (1668) by Pierre Patel (ca. 1605–1676)*

Rondeau Form

A popular form of 18th-century French harpsichord music, the **rondeau**, consists of a **main section** (refrain, rondeau, *grand couplet*, reprise), usually repeated, which alternates with contrasting sections called **couplets** (or episodes). The *grand couplet* is repeated after each couplet. Typically, there were three or four couplets.

François Couperin (1668–1733) was an outstanding harpsichordist, organist and composer whose musical contributions ranked in importance alongside French musicians such as Lully and Rameau.

From several generations of musicians, he became known as "Couperin le Grand" because of his outstanding abilities and to distinguish him from his other well-known family members. The Royal Organist and Court Harpsichordist for Louis XIV, he composed songs, cantatas and other instrumental chamber works, many of which were performed for the King during his regular Sunday concerts. In 1716, he published *L'Art de toucher le clavecin* (The Art of Playing the Harpsichord), which was an important treatise on fingering, ornaments and performance in this period. He is best known for writing over 235 harpsichord pieces, published in four volumes during his lifetime.

Le Petit-Rien

(The Little Nothing)

François Couperin
(1668–1733)

(a) Although Couperin requested his music be played exactly as written, the editor suggests students learn this piece without ornamentation, then add as many ornaments as possible. It is important to maintain the rhythmic flow and capture the character of the music, and this piece can be effective without ornaments.

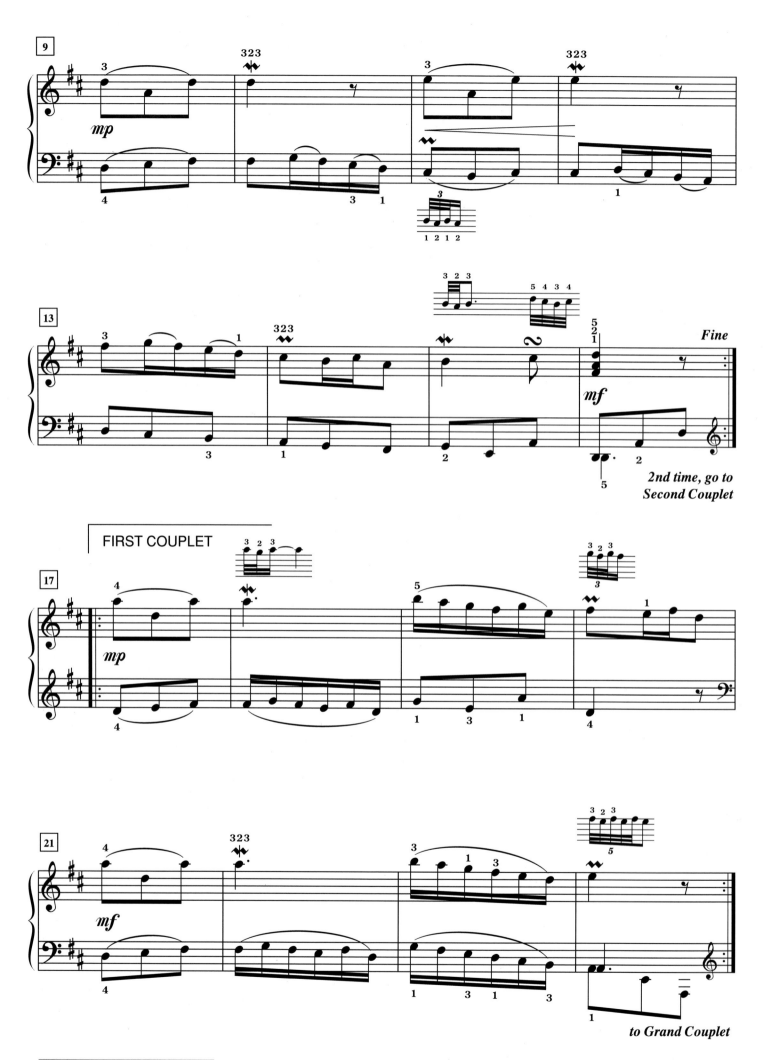

SECOND COUPLET

(a) This ornament, marked by a slur before the trilled note, is a **Pralltriller.** Couperin used this ornament when the note preceding the trill was the same as the upper, or starting note of the trill to avoid its repetition. Play the trill instantly after the beat, or tied note.

to Grand Couplet al Fine

Dance: Rigaudon

Originally a folk dance from southern France, the **rigaudon** was a popular social dance at the Court of Louis XIV. Later as an instrumental form, it was used in French ballets and operas. Couples faced each other and danced a variety of steps, including a slight hop and jump. With an upbeat in duple meter, it typically had four-bar phrases, rather static harmony, and contained a rhythmic accent on the first two measures. A theorist from the time stated that the dance reminded him of sailing or of a **pastoral** (rural, shepherd) scene.

Rigaudon I, II and Variation

Rigaudon I

Jean-Philippe Rameau
(1683–1764)

Rigaudon II

ⓐ Roll the chord slowly from the top down in measures 32 and 52.

Variation

German Musical Life

- A Holy Roman Emperor, who existed in name from 962 to 1806, governed German-speaking lands but had very little real control.

- During the Baroque period, over 300 Germanic cities and states were mostly self-ruled. Some of these cities were major trading centers dominated by middle class merchants, while other regions were governed by small courts, with their own ruler.

- Most German **musicians were employed** either in a court, by a nobleman, or in a city, by a town council or church. The various German kingdoms, duchies, electorates and other principalities had lavish courts with their own orchestra, theater and opera—according to their cultural desires and wealth.

- The French court in Versailles was the model for all European courts, and German aristocrats were sent there to learn its style (manners, dress and language). Most German courts employed a French dancing master and musicians from Italy and France, with native Germans in less prestigious positions.

The Precenter *shows a cantor directing a group of choral students. Copperplate engraving by Christoph Weigel (1654–1725).*

German Town Musicians

As early as the late 1300s, German town councils employed groups of **town pipers** (professional musicians), who had salaries and contracts that listed their duties and privileges. Town pipers first trained for five or six years to master several wind and string instruments before becoming **journeymen**, and by audition could obtain a position. They performed for official celebrations, parades, royal visits, civic weddings, church services, and school festivities, and they helped educate musical apprentices.

The highest position a town musician could hold was **City Cantor**, responsible for all music for the city's main church(es), all civic events and for any schools associated with the church(es). As music required greater technical skill, these more "general musicians" were replaced by instrumental "specialists" trained in newly established conservatories.

For more than 250 years, members of the **Bach family** were town musicians.

German Keyboard Music

The German-speaking lands (Germany/Austria) had outstanding builders of keyboard instruments (organs, harpsichords and the new pianofortes). Because of this and the great number of courts and cities that employed musicians during the Baroque period, a large amount of keyboard music was composed. This music showed foreign influence, yet the composers were able to absorb these elements and create a unique German keyboard style that was imitated internationally in the late 18th century.

J. S. Bach at the Court of King Frederick the Great, playing the organ before the King, May 7th and 8th, 1747 in Potsdam.

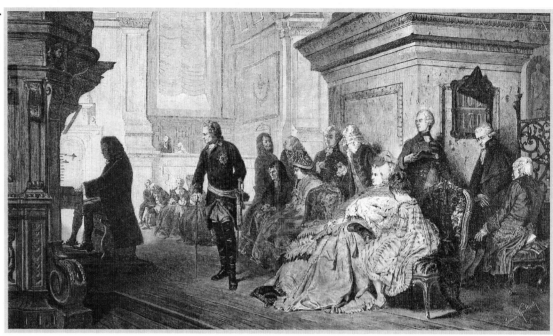

AKG London

"I was obliged to work hard. Whoever is equally industrious will succeed just as well."
Johann Sebastian Bach[13]

Johann Sebastian Bach (1685–1750)

Considered by many to be the greatest composer who ever lived, J. S. Bach was most famous as an organist during his lifetime. He held every type of musical position in Germany and taught private students for over 40 years. A deeply religious man, he believed the primary purpose of his life and works was to glorify God.

- J. S. Bach's father was a town musician. Orphaned at 10, Johann sang in a boy's choir, where he was also educated and given musical instruction. He held positions as organist and Cantor, eventually becoming *Konzertmeister* at the Court in Weimar.

- His most important position was Director of Music and Cantor at St. Thomas's Church for the city of Leipzig. Bach was the town council's third choice. *"Since the best man could not be obtained, lesser ones would have to be accepted,"*[14] stated a town councilman. In Leipzig, Bach was responsible for the music at the four churches, all city events, festive events at the university, and for the musical training of the students at the boarding school.

- Three years before Bach's death, he visited the Court of King Frederick the Great (1712–1786) of Prussia, where his son, Carl Philipp Emanuel Bach (1714–1788), was employed. There he played several new pianofortes.

[13]Crofton and Fraser, *Musical Quotations*, 11.
[14]Machlis, 399.

Prelude

A **prelude** is a free form, usually brief and based on one musical idea.

- Johann Forkel (1749–1817), Bach's first biographer, wrote that Bach taught his keyboard students his way of "touching" the instrument first. For months, they practiced finger exercises. When students lost patience, he combined the exercises into little pieces, including the *Little Preludes* and *Inventions*.

Little Prelude in C Major

Johann Sebastian Bach (1685–1750)
BWV 939

"A good composer should be able to set public notices to music."
Georg Philipp Telemann (1681–1767)[15]

Fantasia

Because the term **fantasia** originally meant an instrumental composition whose form came *"solely from the fantasy and skill of the author who created it,"*[16] there is great variety in pieces with this name. This fantasia has several different **motives** that are then used in **imitation** and **sequences**.

Georg Philipp Telemann, one of the most famous and influential German composers of his day, wrote over 3,000 compositions. Without any formal musical training, by the age of 10 he could play keyboard, flute, violin and zither, and by age 12 had written an opera.

Most of his life was spent as *Kapellmeister* at various German courts and as Cantor for the city of Hamburg, the most prestigious position in Germany. In addition to his required duties, he was the director of the Hamburg Opera and was known as a theorist, teacher and organizer of public concerts.

# Fantasia

Georg Philipp Telemann
(1681–1767)

[15]Crofton and Fraser, *Musical Quotations,* 146.
[16]*New Grove's Dictionary,* "Fantasia" by Christopher Field, Vol. 6, 380.

Invention

An **invention** is a term sometimes used to describe any short instrumental composition in **two-part counterpoint** (two independent voices or parts that fit together). The term "invention" is most associated with the final version of J. S. Bach's *15 Inventions*, composed in 1723. In his title page, Bach wrote that the object of the inventions was *"to teach clear playing in two and three ... parts, good inventions (i.e., compositional ideas), and a cantabile (singing) manner of playing."*[17]

Bach's first requirement of his composition students, according to his son, Carl Philipp Emanuel, was the "invention" of ideas.

Johann Philipp Kirnberger was a German theorist and composer who studied composition and performance with J. S. Bach for two years and tried to publicize "Bach's method."

Principal motive of this invention:

Inversion (intervals in reverse direction) of the motive (transposed to C):

The inversion of the motive appears only once, in the first measure of the piece, both of which are very unusual.

Invention

Johann Philipp Kirnberger
(1721–1783)

[17]*New Grove's Dictionary*, "J. S. Bach," Vol. 1, 813.

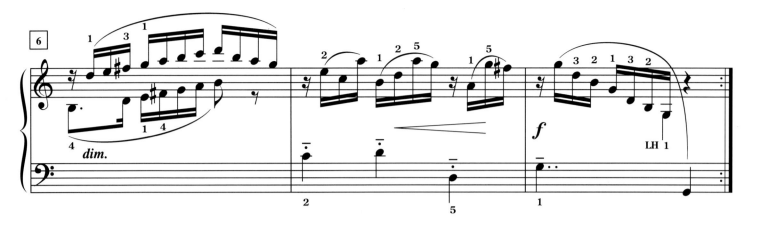

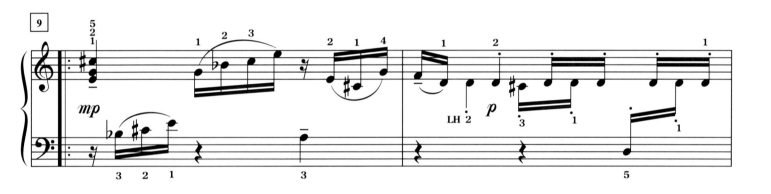

Invention No. 8 in F Major

Johann Sebastian Bach (1685–1750)
BWV 779

Other Baroque Dances

Dances from the Baroque period had a great influence on keyboard music. Dance forms already included are: gavotte (page 25), tambourin (page 33), menuet (page 35), and rigaudon (page 40). Following are some other Baroque dances: musette (page 54), hornpipe (page 58), sarabande (page 59), and chaconne (page 60). Other important dances of the Baroque period include: gigue, allemande, bourrée, polonaise, and courante.

Musette

■ A **musette** was a small bagpipe fashionable at the French courts of Louis XIV and Louis XV. The bags for these musettes were sometimes elaborately decorated and covered with fine materials. Some pipes were made of ivory and inlaid with jewels. Treatises were written describing the instrument and how to play it.

■ Music included musette duets, songs accompanied by musette and ensembles with other instruments.

■ The moderate tempo **dance** (part of French ballets) usually had a drone bass with the treble moving in stepwise motion. Ladies and gentlemen of the court would perform in pastoral costumes (often as shepherds and peasants).

■ The character is similar to a **gavotte** (see page 25). A theorist in 1789 stated keyboard musettes should be played in a "coaxing and slurred"[18] manner.

[18] *New Grove's Dictionary,* "Musette" by Anthony Baines, Vol. 12, 797.

A musette played by a Baroque court musician

Musette

from the *Notebook for Anna Magdalena Bach* (1725)

Johann Sebastian Bach (1685–1750)
BWV Anh. 126

Johann Friedrich Gräfe was an amateur German poet and composer who earned his living as a postal clerk and court secretary. He published four collection of songs that had several printings. Eight of the pieces in his collections (including this one) were copied by Leopold Mozart into the notebook for his son, Wolfgang Amadeus.

usette

Johann Friedrich Gräfe
(1711–1787)

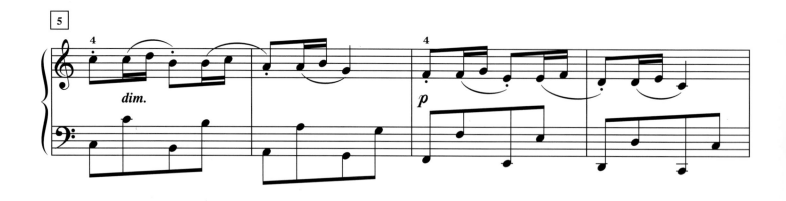

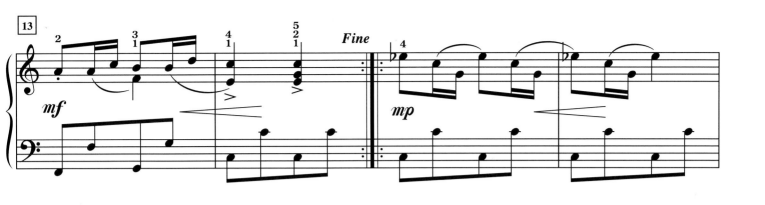

Hornpipe

A **hornpipe** was a folk instrument with one or two pipes, sounded by an attached reed. At the end of the pipe is a cowhorn or two. A dance resembling a **jig** was also known as a **hornpipe** in the British Isles, since the instrument was used to accompany it.

Henry Purcell, one of the finest English composers of his time, wrote in all vocal and instrumental forms. A member of the King's Chapel, he composed for the Court. Later he served as organist at Westminster Abbey where he is buried.

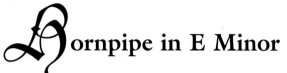
Hornpipe in E Minor

Henry Purcell
(1659–1695)

Sarabande

Sarabandes, originally a dance from Latin America and Spain, had become extremely popular in European courts by 1650.

- The French style of the Sarabande was most common in keyboard music from the time of Louis XIV.

- Usually written in two sections, Sarabandes are dignified in spirit and are similar in character to the **folia** and the **chaconne**.

- Majestic rhythms are characteristic. Although the dance is in triple meter, there are frequent accents on the second beat.

Typical sarabande rhythm:

Johann Pachelbel, known today for his *Canon in D*, spent most of his life as an organist at various courts and churches in Germany. He wrote music for violins and continuo, choirs, and solo harpsichord. His organ works, especially his **chorale preludes** (preludes based on hymn melodies), influenced J. S. Bach.

Sarabande

Johann Pachelbel
(1653–1706)

Variation: Chaconne

A **chaconne** was a Baroque dance from Latin America that became popular in Spain, Italy and France. In France, it became slow and dignified but maintained its triple meter.

Certain harmonies were used as accompaniment to the dance. These bass melodies were used throughout Europe in a type of **continuous variation**. The chaconne has a **repeated bass line** (ostinato or ground bass), so the theme is a succession of chords (controlled by the interval of a fourth) that gives a harmonic basis to the variations.

Johann Caspar Ferdinand Fischer, one of the best keyboard performers of his day, spent most of his life as *Kapellmeister* (music director) to the Margrave of Baden, whose court reflected French taste. Fischer's series of 20 preludes and fugues, all in different keys, is a forerunner of Bach's *Well Tempered Clavier*.

Chaconne

Johann Caspar Ferdinand Fischer
(ca. 1670–1746)

Variation I

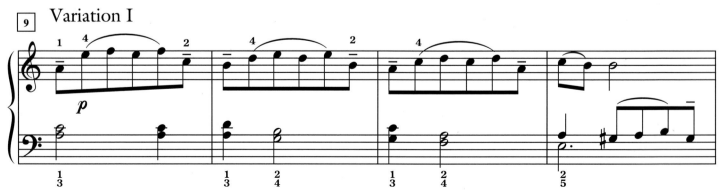

English Musical Life

When the monarchy was restored, court life became less extravagant and foreign ideas and conventions became fashionable. This was somewhat due to the Hanover family of Germany becoming the Kings in England.

By the turn of the 18th century, England was a world power and London a leading commercial center. Public concerts first became important in England. With a concert-going public; music publishing flourishing; and amateurs wanting lessons, music and keyboard instruments, foreign musicians flocked to London to seek their fortune.

G. F. Handel and King George I of England on the River Thames during a performance of "Water Music."

AKG London

George Frideric Handel (1685–1759)

George Frideric Handel was the first composer whose music has continually been performed since his death.

- Born in Halle, Germany, he played in the orchestra at the opera house in Hamburg, where his operas were later produced. Invited to Florence, he also went to Rome and became a successful producer of operas in Italy.

- Becoming *Kapellmeister* at the Court in Hanover, Germany, he took a leave to visit London. His operas were a huge success with the public, in spite of critics who thought performing Italian opera in England was absurd. He spent the next 50 years there.

- When Queen Anne died, Handel's former employer became King George I of England. Handel produced operas for the English public. After several years, public taste changed, and he went bankrupt.

- Next he produced oratorios; his most famous being the *Messiah*, which he wrote in three weeks. He dominated music in London during this time. He wrote works on demand for the royal family and for state occasions. He also performed in taverns, played the organ at St. Paul's Cathedral, conducted his operas and oratorios, and performed as organ soloist during intermissions.

- Over 3,000 Londoners attended his funeral at Westminster Abbey where he is buried.

[19]Crofton and Fraser, *Musical Quotations,* 72.

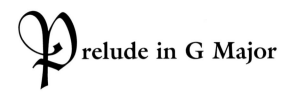relude in G Major

George Frideric Handel
(1685–1759)

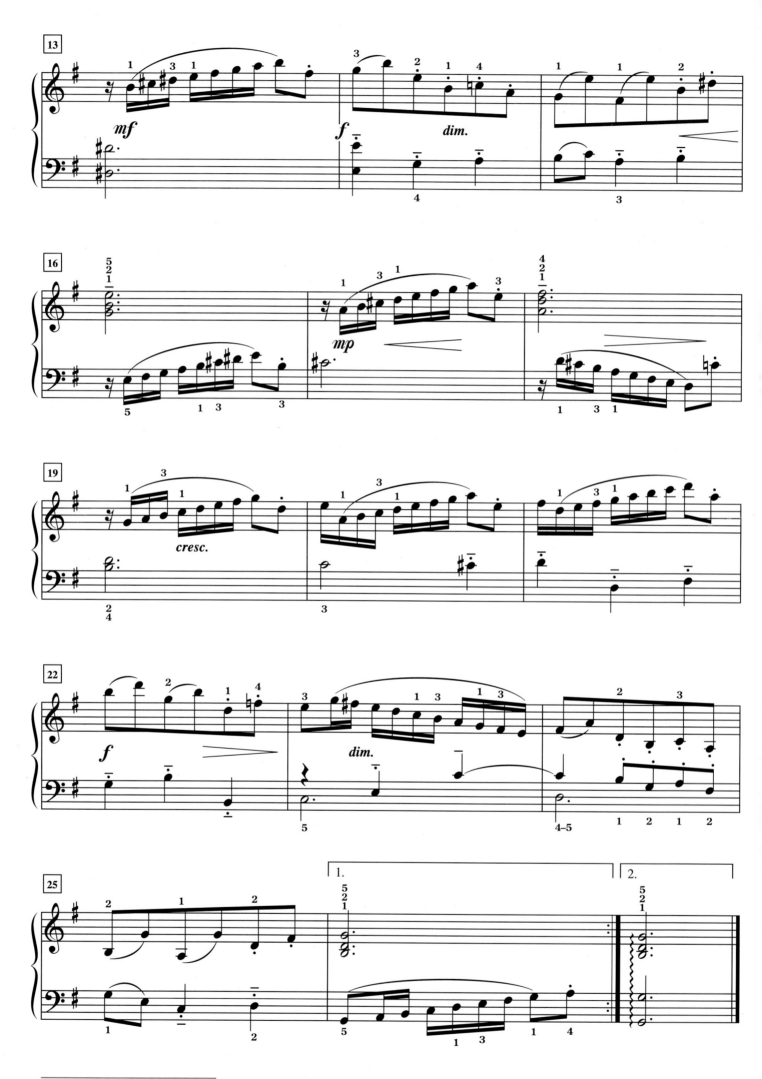